This book belongs to:

....

AUTUMN
PUBLISHING

Published in 2022
First published in the UK by Autumn Publishing
An imprint of Igloo Books Ltd
Cottage Farm, NN6 0BJ, UK
Owned by Bonnier Books
Sveavägen 56, Stockholm, Sweden
www.autumnpublishing.co.uk

0522 004
2 4 6 8 10 9 7 5 3
ISBN 978-1-83903-200-4

Written by Suzanne Fossey
Illustrated by Gisela Bohórquez

Designed by Lee Italiano
Edited by Suzanne Fossey

Printed and manufactured in China

The Life of a Little
PLASTIC BOTTLE

AUTUMN
PUBLISHING

I was sitting with the other bottles, lined up on the shelf,
When a customer got thirsty, and took me for herself.

I was happy to be useful,
as she carried me along,

Gulping at the
water until **every**
drop was **gone.**

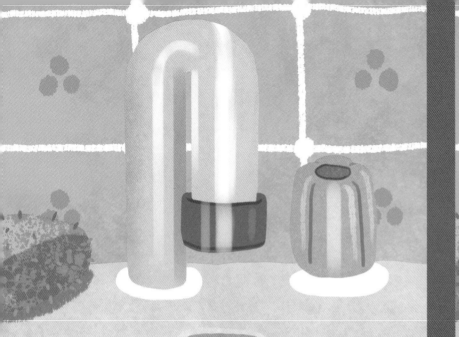

But she didn't put me in the trash,
she took me to the sink.
Whoooooosh!

She turned the tap on.
I didn't know what
to think!

The water really **tickled.**
I'd never felt like
that before.

The tap went off, my lid
went on and I was
full once more.

Snug inside a rucksack, I went all the way to school.
I gave my owner lots of sips of water to keep cool.

At breaktime, while the children played, I sat beneath a tree.
How nice to see so many other bottles just like me!

I heard a squeal of laughter and
someone plucked me from my spot.
They let me join in with their games.
It made me laugh a lot!

But when the sun went down, the children all went home,
And I was left there on the ground, cold and all alone.

Suddenly I heard a voice,
and woke up with a flash.

"When will those children learn to
put their rubbish in the trash?

"Come on, little bottle.
You can help me show them how."

The teacher
picked me
up.

I wondered
what would
happen now.

The teacher told her class
they shouldn't throw plastic away.
Reduce, reuse, recycle is
by far the better way.

To show them how,
she worked on me with
scissors, glue and string,
And made a lovely bird
feeder, for bluebirds on
the wing.

One windy day, I toppled down, and landed on the ground.
I stayed there for a while until a fox came sniffing round.

"Please don't eat
my lovely string or give
my spoon a chew!"

"Don't worry,
little bottle.
I'm just passing through.
I can't eat you, you're not food.
You'll just make me sick.
Wild animals like me
can **never** eat
plastic."

The fox went on his way. I was **alone** once more.
Then someone else came walking by and **picked** me off the floor.

They put me in a bin with **bottles** of every size.
We wondered what would happen next.
It was a **big** surprise!

Next morning, we were gathered up by a garbage crew.

They took us to a factory where we were made brand new.

I could
have been,
well, anything:
a brush
or ball
or model.

But I became
a bright and shiny
brand-new...

... plastic bottle.

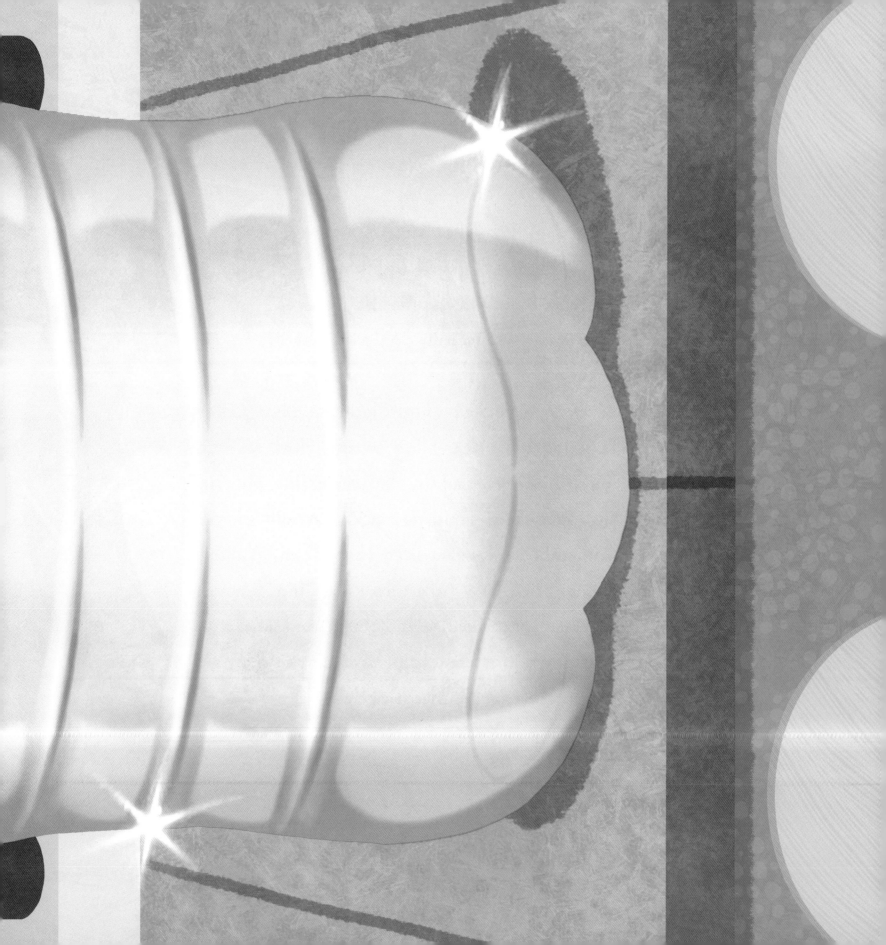

When you have finished drinking from your plastic bottle, there are many ways you can still use it. You could turn it into a bird feeder, a pretty vase, or even a rocket ship! You can also put it in a recycling bin. Recycling means that we use things over and over again. By recycling plastic, we make sure that it is not accidentally eaten by wild animals or thrown into the ocean. Millions of plastic bottles are taken to recycling centres each day. They are melted down and made into anything from toys and clothing, to new plastic bottles.